Songbirds